First Paperback Edition Dec. 2021
Copyright© 2021 by Jeremiah Raber
ISBN: 9798778609976

D1361565

GROWING UP AMISH
A CHILDREN'S STORY

By: Jeremiah Raber

Left Blank on Purpose

My name's Johnny, and I grew up Amish in the great state of Ohio. Some kids might laugh at that or think it's old-fashioned. It might seem that way to some. A lot of people don't know what being Amish means, so I'd like to tell you my story.

To me, it meant being part of a hardworking, loving family. Being part of a community that helped each other. And, most of all, living a good life like my parents did and their parents before them and so on.

I grew up on a farm, so I got up around six o'clock in the morning. With the sun peeking over the horizon, I'd run to the barn where I milked the cows.

Sometimes I'd talk to them. Sometimes I'd even sing to them, and it seemed to make them happy! They all had their own names, like Dorothy and Eleanor.

After my chores, I dashed back to the house, where Mother would have breakfast waiting. Hot oatmeal and some fruit, enough to give me energy for my walk to school. Before that, though, I took a quick bath. Now I was refreshed and ready.

Then I dashed off, saying goodbye to Mother and Father and walked the one and a half miles to school. There I sat, in a schoolhouse that was only one room. Everyone studied, and our teacher seemed to know just about everything! You might have seen something like it on your television, I'm sure.

After school, I ran back home, making it just in time to play with my dog, Sparky. He always loved to run with me.

We'd run through the fields, down the road, and back again. She also had puppies, and when they arrived, soon they were running with us, too.

After playtime, it was back to chores. All the Amish kids did chores, and it was just a part of life. Everyone helped out on the farm; that's how we lived. We worked hard, and everything turned out all right.

So, I'd do some more milking, cleaning, feeding, and anything else Mother or Father asked of me.

Then, it was time for a hearty dinner. Sometimes Mother would make steak and mashed potatoes. Sometimes she'd make us a layered dinner with vegetables and sausage. And there was always freshly baked bread! And, if I was good, I'd get some Cherry Delight for dessert.

Oh, and you might not know, but I'll tell you anyway. Often we'd speak our language at home, which is Pennsylvania Dutch. I suppose it's really German, but most Amish like my family speak it.

After dinner, I couldn't grab my fishing rod fast enough. You see, we had a big fishing pond on our farm. Yes, that's right! And every evening, I'd be out there, fishing until the sun went down.

Sparky and her puppies would sometimes join me. Other times, Father might come and fish for a bit, too. Mostly, though, it was just me alone with my thoughts. And the fish, of course.

Then it was time for bed. I'd say goodnight to Mother and Father, say my prayers, and then grab a book.

There was nothing quite like reading in bed. Sometimes by candlelight, and other times by the light of the moon. And before I knew it, I was fast asleep.

Yet another day would begin. And so went my days, until finally, the weekend arrived.

On those days, after chores, you'd find me wandering through the woods. Sometimes reading a favorite book or just laying against a log and relaxing as the sun crossed overhead.

We Amish enjoy nature, God's creation, every single day.

Now, as school drew to a close and summer arrived, it was a special time. For many kids who aren't Amish, this means vacations, summer camps, and days spent doing nothing at all.

But I grew up Amish, and summer was for work. Why? Well, I grew up on a farm. And the summer was for baling hay, plowing, and whatever else needed to be done.

"Wait a minute," some might say. "How do you bale hay and plow without modern machinery?"

We use the oldest machines around: horses and old-fashioned machines. That's right.

Father would prepare the baler, attach the horses, and off they'd go. He'd steer the horses carefully, moving across the field, baling the grass into hay.

And yes, we'd use horse-power for plowing the earth, too. I'd always love watching and helping to hitch the horses.

Some used seven horses, and some used twelve. We used six ourselves, and those horses worked hard. And we did, too!

Steering the horses was not easy at all. I tried once before I was old enough, and those horses wouldn't listen at all. Father finally showed me when I was tall and strong enough, and then I helped him plow the fields.

But it wasn't all work during the summer. I still played in the woods and went fishing. It just meant there was a lot to do, even when there wasn't any school to attend. Still, I would study my Bible and read my books.

And coming in for dinner after those long summer days was the best. Mother prepared meals for everyone, and we kids enjoyed big hearty meals together. I was so stuffed afterward.

After getting dirty in the woods and fields, I'd take a bath. I imagined the next day and what I'd do. Maybe I'd catch a few more fish, and maybe Father would teach me something new.

Every day there was something to be learned, and I was excited to learn new things. People think Amish live in a time capsule, and sure, maybe we do. But it doesn't make life any less exciting, especially for a young boy or girl like yourself.

Oh, and one last thing. Before I'd pick up my book to read, I'd wind my special clock. Mother gave me one, a beautiful mechanical clock. So, that would close out my day.

Then everything was done, and it was time to read, imagine, and fall asleep again. And then I'd be ready for another day, being an Amish boy in Ohio.

THE END

Please visit my website
https://www.jeremiahraber.com